SUPERMAN ANNUAL 2015

Published in the UK by Titan Comics, a division of Titan Publishing Group Ltd, 144 Southwark St, London SE1 0UP.

First edition: August 2014
ISBN: 978-1-78276-190-7
TCN: 0325
10 9 8 7 6 5 4 3 2 1

A CIP catalogue record for this title is available from the British Library.

EDITORIAL
Editors: Neil Edwards
Designer: Russ Seal

TITAN COMICS
Senior Comics Editor: Martin Eden
Production Supervisors: Maria Pearson and Jackie Flook
Art Director: Oz Browne
Studio Manager: Selina Juneja
Circulation Manager: Steve Tothill
Marketing Manager: Ricky Claydon
Marketing Assistant: Jaleesa Lynsdale
Advertising Manager: Michelle Fairlamb
Publishing Manager: Darryl Tothill
Publishing Director: Chris Teather
Operations Director: Leigh Baulch
Executive Director: Vivian Cheung
Publisher: Nick Landau

PRINTED IN ITALY

SUPERMAN®

ANNUAL 2015

TM

TITAN COMICS

"BORED.

"BORED.

"BORED.

"BORED."

"OH, LOIS LANE, COME ON.

"ONE AFTERNOON WITHOUT AN ALIEN INVASION OR A SUPER-VILLAIN ATTACK ISN'T GOING TO KILL YOU."

"DON'T BE SO SURE, SMALLVILLE. I LIVE ON EXCITEMENT."

DAILY PLANET

AND ANOTHER DAY OF SITTING AROUND HERE WAITING FOR AN ASTEROID TO HIT US ISN'T GOING TO CUT IT.

I LIKE THE PEACE AND QUIET, PERSONALLY.

REMINDS ME OF MY DAYS INTERNING AT THE SMALLVILLE TORCH--

UGH. DON'T REMINISCE, CLARK. MY SANITY CAN ONLY STAND SO MUCH FOLKSINESS--

OKAY, GOT SOMETHING--

MINE!
IT'S A--
I DON'T CARE--
DOG SHOW.
YOU'RE KILLING ME, PERRY.
KILLING ME.
I'LL DO IT, MR. WHITE, NO PROBLEM.
YEAH, I BET.
Y'KNOW, LOIS, THEY SAY A GREAT REPORTER CAN FIND A STORY ANYWHERE.
DO THEY REALLY, SMALLVILLE?
OKAY THEN...

"YOU'RE ON. BEST STORY GETS THE BYLINE."
TAKE ME TO THE SHUSTER CENTER, PLEASE--
LOIS! WAIT UP, WE CAN SHARE A CAB--
LOSERS SHARE CABS, CLARK!
HMPH.
HEEEELLLLLLPPP MEEEEE!
DOG SHOW'S GOING TO HAVE TO WAIT--
355
DUTY CALLS.
NO NEED TO FEAR, MA'AM--
WHOA. WHAT IS GOING ON?

EESH.

OKAY, BOY, CALM DOWN... LET'S GET YOU HOME--
HEY!

BACK OFF!

RAWR!

48 SECONDS LATER...
THANK YOU, SUPERMAN, YOU SAVED--
NO PROBLEM, MA'AM, BUT I GOTTA GO--
SNIFF
AW, MAN.
THANK YOU, SUPERMAN!
ALL IN A DAY'S WORK, SIR!

C'MON, CLARK, NO PROBLEM. YOU'LL STILL GET THERE BEFORE--
OH, COME ON--
NO ONE WILL STOP THE TOYMAN! NOT EVEN SUP--

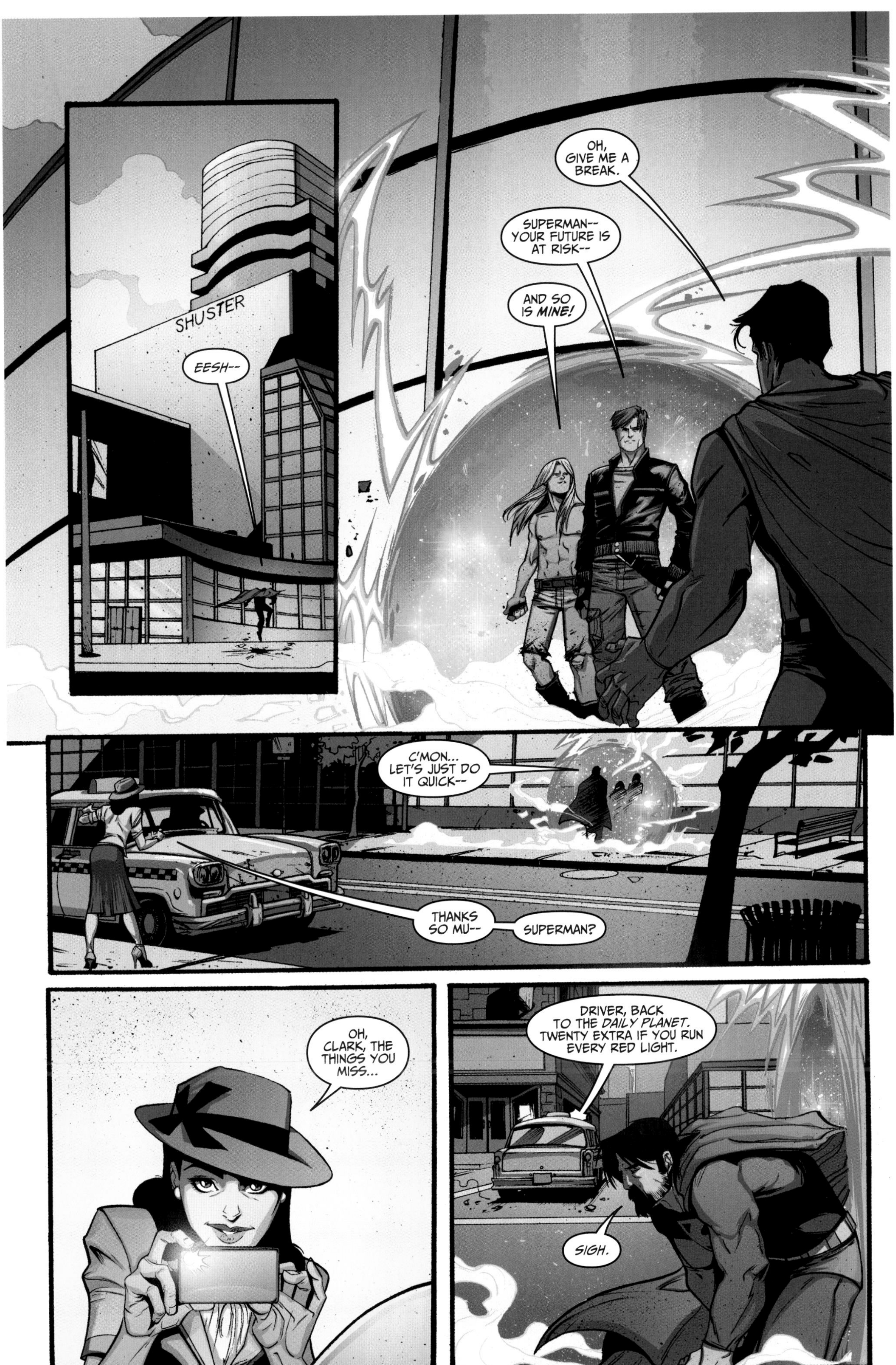

SHUSTER
EESH--
SUPERMAN-- YOUR FUTURE IS AT RISK--
AND SO IS *MINE!*
OH, GIVE ME A BREAK.

C'MON... LET'S JUST DO IT QUICK--
THANKS SO MU--
SUPERMAN?

OH, CLARK, THE THINGS YOU MISS...

DRIVER, BACK TO THE *DAILY PLANET.* TWENTY EXTRA IF YOU RUN EVERY RED LIGHT.
SIGH.

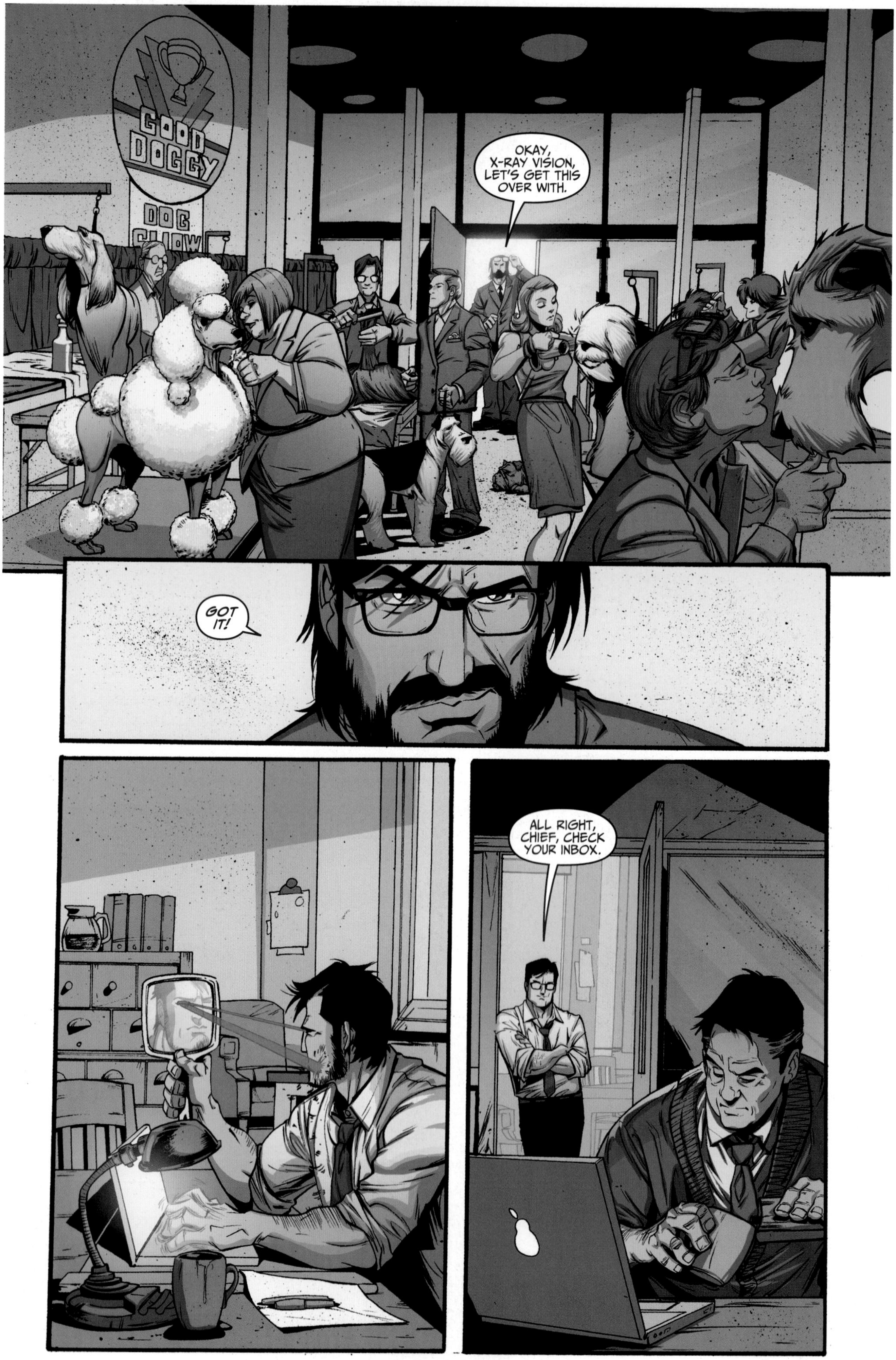

GOOD DOGGY

DOG SHOW

OKAY, X-RAY VISION, LET'S GET THIS OVER WITH.

GOT IT!

THIS IS TERRIFIC, CLARK. GREAT WORK.
FRONT PAGE OF THE LOCAL NEWS SECTION--
SO MINE'S BETTER THAN LOIS'S?
SHE DIDN'T WRITE HERS.
WHAT? WHY NOT?
WHILE YOU WERE LOOKING AT DOGS, SHE WAS BUSY FOLLOWING SUPERMAN ALL OVER TOWN.
IT'S THE FRONT PAGE OF THE LATE EDITION.
DAILY PLANET
SUPERMAN'S BAKER'S DOZEN
YOU REALLY SHOULD TRY *CHASING* THE STORY, CLARK, RATHER THAN JUST TAKING WHAT'S HANDED TO YOU.
BUT OUR BET--
BET? CLARK, THIS IS THE *NEWS*. WHAT WE DO IS MORE *IMPORTANT* THAN A SILLY *BET!*
I...
IF IT MAKES YOU FEEL ANY BETTER, SMALLVILLE, YOU WON. CONGRATS.
NOW, HOW ABOUT WE GO CELEBRATE OUR PAGE ONES?
SIGH.
YOU BET, LOIS.

SLOW NEWS DAY

Joshua Hale Fialkov - Writer
Joëlle Jones - Artist
Nick Filardi - Colorist
Wes Abbott - Letterer
Alex Antone - Editor
Camuncoli & Aviña - Cover

Superman created by
Jerry Siegel & Joe Shuster
By special arrangement with
the Jerry Siegel family.

END

METROPOLIS

The land where Metropolis now stands was settled in 1702 by the Dutch who found the inlet location perfect for ships from the old world to harbor. The settlement withheld British forces during the Revolutionary War, most notably the legendary "Devil's Winter Siege," thanks to the valiant efforts of Tomahawk and his rangers, especially Dan Hunter, in whose honor the settlement was renamed Fort Hunter (later Hunterville). By the 1800s, Hunter City was a thriving community deriving most of its economy from shipping and importing as well as their iron works, supplying tools and metal products to points farther west. It was with the arrival of legendary adventurer and science hero Waldo Glenmorgan that the city first became a hub for scientific discovery. Turner City's nickname "Metropolis" became its official name in 1905, by which time many more scientists and inventors had settled on the east side of town from where the Avenue of Tomorrow first sprang. Today, Metropolis is the leading city for science and invention in America, boasting labs and facilities that produce more than half of the world's technological advancements.

1. LEXCORP Towering over the west end of the city, the LexCorp building was built by Lex Luthor to stand as a testament not only to modern science, but also to Lex's own genius. Since Lex Luthor became a fugitive, no CEO has lasted more than a few months, and the future of LexCorp remains uncertain...

2. THE DAILY STAR BUILDING Owned by famed millionaire recluse Morgan Edge, the Star Building is home to the Daily Star, the Daily Planet's newspaper rival, and the WGBS news television network.

3. WAYNETECH The newly erected WayneTech Tower serves as a counterpoint to LexCorp.

4. THE DAILY PLANET The home of Metropolis's number one newspaper.

5. HAMMERSMITH TOWER The residence of Lana and Linda Lang.

6. 1938 SULLIVAN PLACE The residence of Clark Kent and Lois Lane.

7. METROPOLIS POLICE PRECINCT #55 Home of the recently founded Metropolis MetaCrimes unit, which is headed by Police Inspector Mike Henderson.

8. SHUSTER SPORTS ARENA The playing field of the Metropolis Meteors, Metropolis's first baseball team. Their crosstown rivalry with the Metropolis Monarchs is legendary.

9. CENTENNIAL PARK Centennial Park is Metropolis's largest public park. At the center of the park is a statue of Superman, erected after his seemingly fatal fight with the monster known as Doomsday, as well as a statue of Superboy.

10. GLENMORGAN SQUARE Also called "Metro Square." A busy crossroads of art and commerce, Glenmorgan Square is one of the most highly trafficked areas of the city, drawing tourists from all over the world.

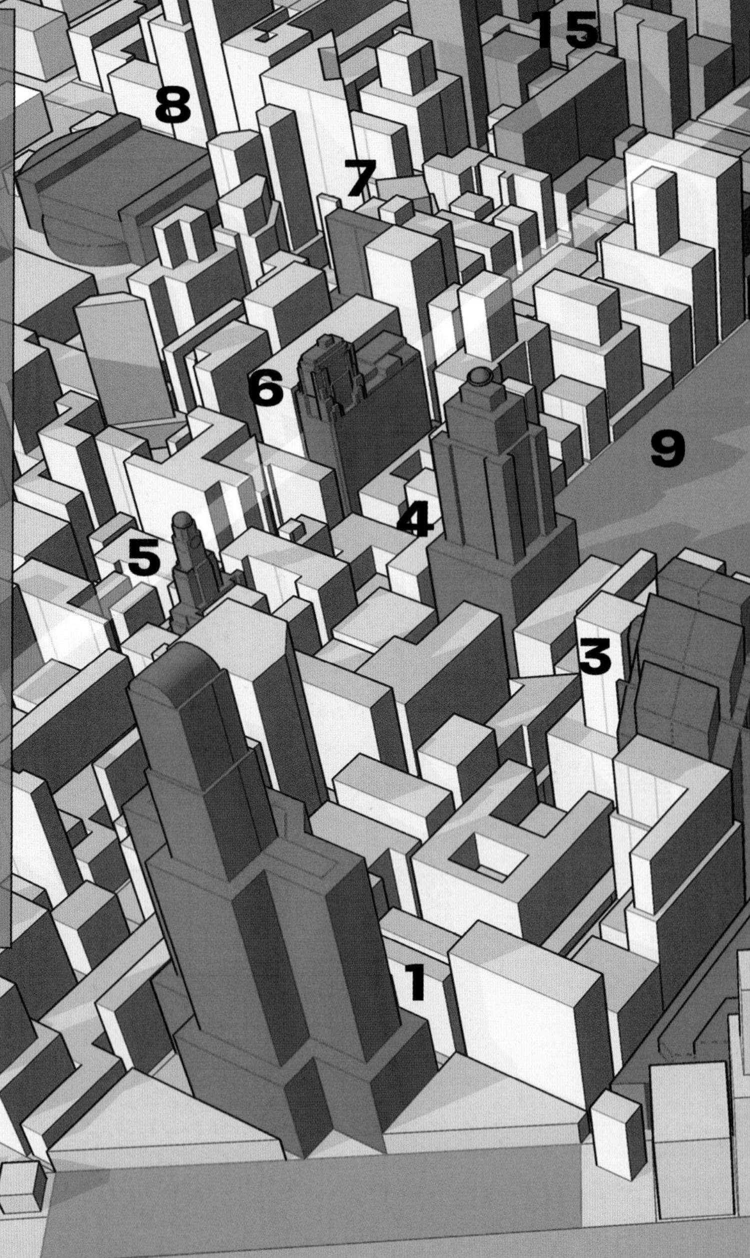

11. KINDLE TOWERS The residence of Dr. Kimiyo Hoshi, also known as Dr. Light.

12. S.T.A.R. LABS The main facility of the Scientific and Technological Advanced Research Laboratories, to which all other S.T.A.R. branches report.

13. UNIVERSITY OF METROPOLIS A private university specializing in "the minds of tomorrow," Met. U employs some of the finest scientific minds in the world to serve as professors.

14. THE METRO FINANCIAL DISTRICT The headquarters of the city's major financial institutions. The streets of this district are always buzzing with the biggest trades of the day.

15. THE WONDERLAND DISTRICT Home to dozens of the top scientific companies in the world, including Cale-Anderson Pharmaceuticals, Dayton Industries, Tyler Chemicals, Magnus Robotics, Vulcan Industries, and Stagg Enterprises.

16. 8006 PAPP AVENUE The residence of Mon-El's alter ego, Jonathan Kent.

17. SCIENCE POLICE HEADQUARTERS Built directly across from Stryker's Island, the Science Police HQ stands ever vigilant against a metahuman breakout.

18. STRYKER'S ISLAND The ultimate in maximum security, Stryker's features custom-made high-tech prison cells to accommodate its metahuman inmates.

Text by JAMES ROBINSON & STERLING GATES, art & color by PETE WOODS

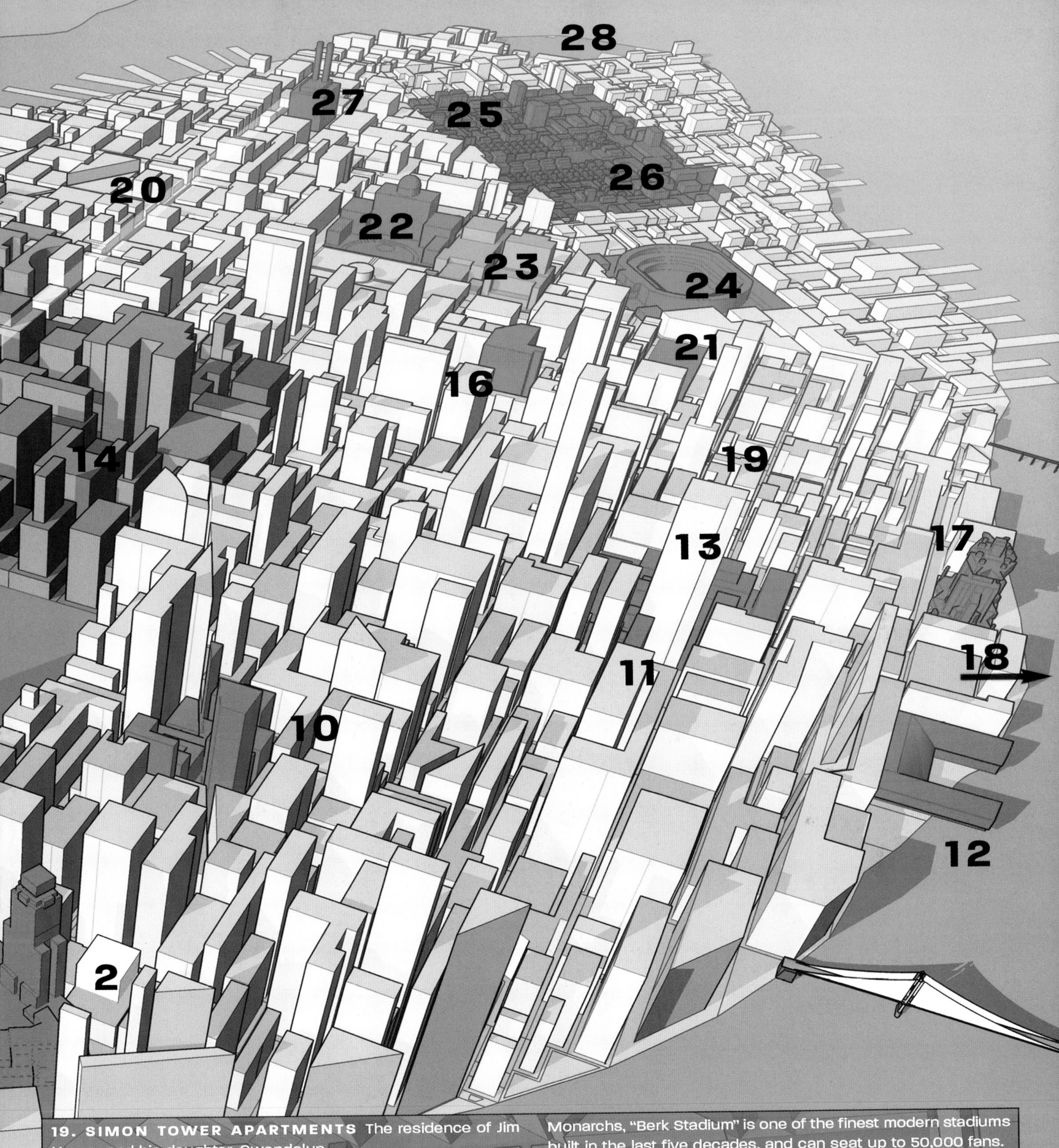

19. SIMON TOWER APARTMENTS The residence of Jim Harper and his daughter, Gwendolyn.

20. THE AVENUE OF TOMORROW The Avenue of Tomorrow is the main thoroughfare of Metropolis, stretching the entire length of the island.

21. VALHALLA CEMETERY The sole cemetery in Metropolis was established in 1788 and serves as the final resting place for civilians and heroes alike, including Jade and Dr. Fate.

22. METROPOLIS CITY HALL The house of the administrative offices of the municipal government, including the offices of Mayor Margaret Roath.

23. THE CONRAD B. MONTGOMERY FEDERAL BUILDING The regional offices of the FBI, DEA, ATF, and DEO are all housed here.

24. FRANK BERKOWITZ MEMORIAL STADIUM The home ballpark of the Metropolis Monarchs, "Berk Stadium" is one of the finest modern stadiums built in the last five decades, and can seat up to 50,000 fans.

25. ACE O' CLUBS Sitting on "the Avenue of Yesterday," the Ace O' Clubs is the best spot in the city to get a drink. Every Friday night it's packed with all types of people, from blue-collar workers to financial district bigwigs.

26. SUICIDE SLUM Also known as Hob's Bay, Suicide Slum is the most crime-ridden section of Metropolis. Many heroes have tried to help build the area back up over the years, but all have failed.

27. IRON WORKS Originally called Steel Works, Iron Works is where John Henry Irons creates technological wonders to help all mankind.

28. OVERLOOK PARK Overlook Park is the easternmost point of the island. The Sullivan Fountains in the center of the park are the most popular playground for children during hot Metropolis summers.

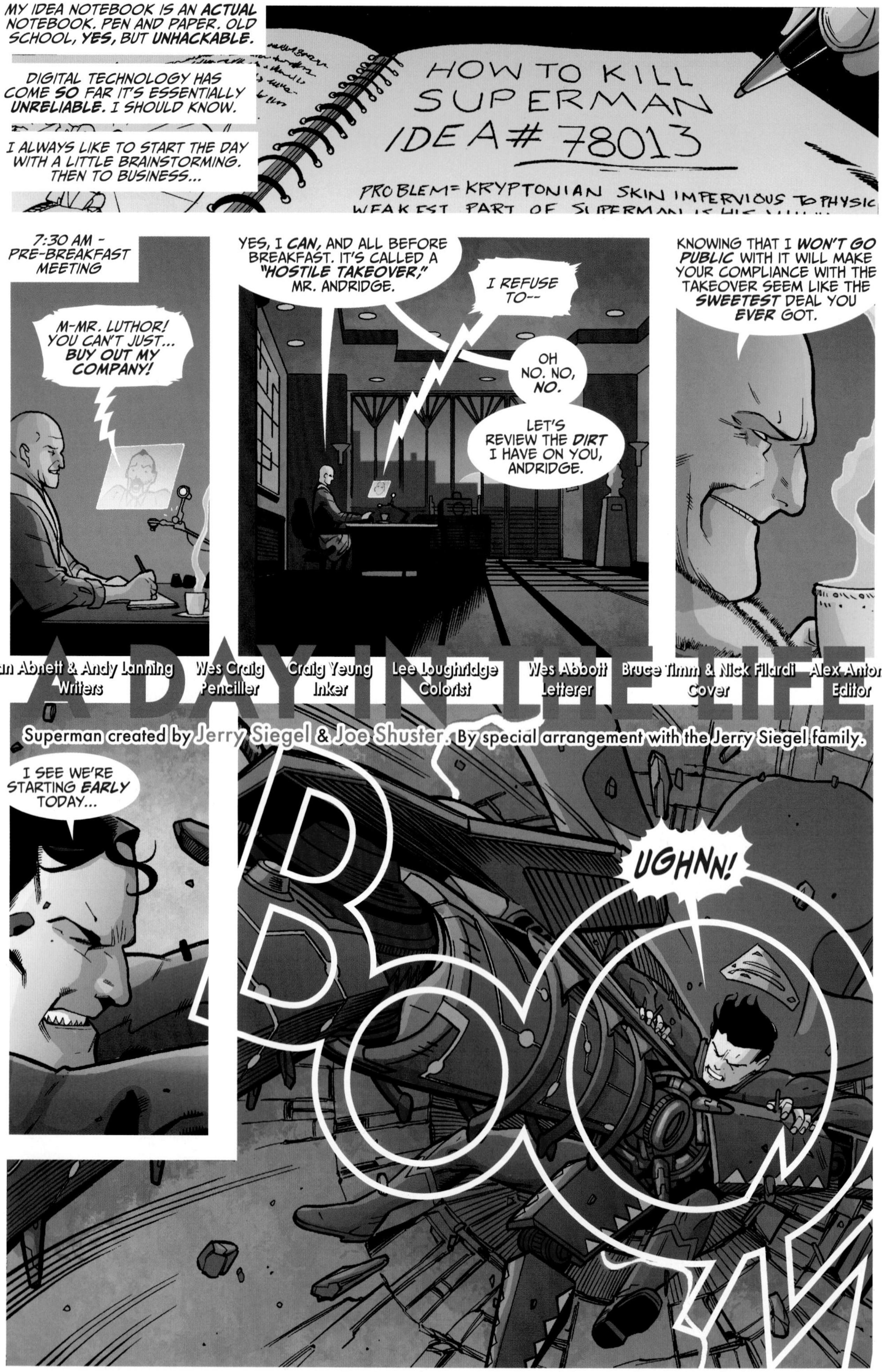

MY IDEA NOTEBOOK IS AN **ACTUAL** NOTEBOOK. PEN AND PAPER. OLD SCHOOL, **YES**, BUT **UNHACKABLE**.

DIGITAL TECHNOLOGY HAS COME **SO** FAR IT'S ESSENTIALLY **UNRELIABLE**. I SHOULD KNOW.

I ALWAYS LIKE TO START THE DAY WITH A LITTLE BRAINSTORMING. THEN TO BUSINESS...

HOW TO KILL SUPERMAN
IDEA # 78013
PROBLEM= KRYPTONIAN SKIN IMPERVIOUS TO PHYSIC
WEAKEST PART OF SUPERMAN IS HIS

7:30 AM - PRE-BREAKFAST MEETING

M-MR. LUTHOR! YOU CAN'T JUST... **BUY OUT MY COMPANY!**

YES, I **CAN,** AND ALL BEFORE BREAKFAST. IT'S CALLED A **"HOSTILE TAKEOVER,"** MR. ANDRIDGE.

I REFUSE TO--

OH NO. NO, **NO.**

LET'S REVIEW THE **DIRT** I HAVE ON YOU, ANDRIDGE.

KNOWING THAT I **WON'T GO PUBLIC** WITH IT WILL MAKE YOUR COMPLIANCE WITH THE TAKEOVER SEEM LIKE THE **SWEETEST** DEAL YOU **EVER** GOT.

A DAY IN THE LIFE

Dan Abnett & Andy Lanning Writers · Wes Craig Penciller · Craig Yeung Inker · Lee Loughridge Colorist · Wes Abbott Letterer · Bruce Timm & Nick Filardi Cover · Alex Antone Editor

I SEE WE'RE STARTING EARLY TODAY...
UGHNN!
BOOOM

7:50 AM - SHOWER AND MANICURE
8:29 AM - ARRIVE AT OFFICE
DOORSTEPPING ME AT MY PLACE OF WORK? **REALLY?**

GOVERNMENT DELEGATIONS THESE DAYS! NO **CLASS!**

MR. LUTHOR, YOU MADE A **COMMITMENT** TO SUPPLY US WITH **BREAKTHROUGH MANUFACTURING PATENTS** TO HELP THE TANKING ECONOMY--

YES, IN EXCHANGE FOR **YOU** TURNING A BLIND EYE TO MY **OFF-BOOK** ACTIVITIES.
THAT IS **ABSOLUTELY** ASSURED! NO OVERSIGHT COMMITTEES! NO JUDICIAL SCRUTINY! NO--

GOOD, THEN! **FINE!**
SEE MY SECRETARY. SHE'LL SORT YOU OUT WITH SOMETHING.

I THINK THERE'S A **COLD-FUSION AUTOMOBILE** I'VE LOST INTEREST IN.
AND SOME **RADICAL** CYBERNETICS, BUT WHO NEEDS A NOBEL?

BOOM
OKAY, YOU'RE BIG **AND** MEAN.
GOTTA GET YOU CLEAR OF **PUBLIC SPACES.**

9:01 AM - AT-DESK WORK REVIEW
--FIGHTING AN OUT-OF-CONTROL GIANT ROBOT IN DOWNTOWN METROPOLIS--
--GLOBAL SHARES PRICES NOW--
--AND CUTTING TO WORLD NEWS--
ARE YOU READY FOR YOUR 9:15, SIR? YOU SAID YOU WANTED TO HANDLE THE GENOME DIVISION THING PERSONALLY?
OH, YEAH. GET THOSE GUYS IN HERE!

OKAY, PEOPLE. GOOD TO SEE YOU.
BIG HONOR, I KNOW, TO COME UP HERE FOR SOME FACE-TIME. YOU'VE BEEN WORKING FOR ME FOR SEVEN YEARS NOW. WE'VE NEVER MET.
NOW I KNOW I CAN EASILY DELEGATE THIS TO HUMAN RESOURCES, BECAUSE I AM VERY BUSY, BUT FOR ME THIS IS A BRIGHT SPOT IN THE DAY.
I JUST LOVE TO BE ABLE TO SEE YOUR FACES. IT'S A PERSONAL THING.

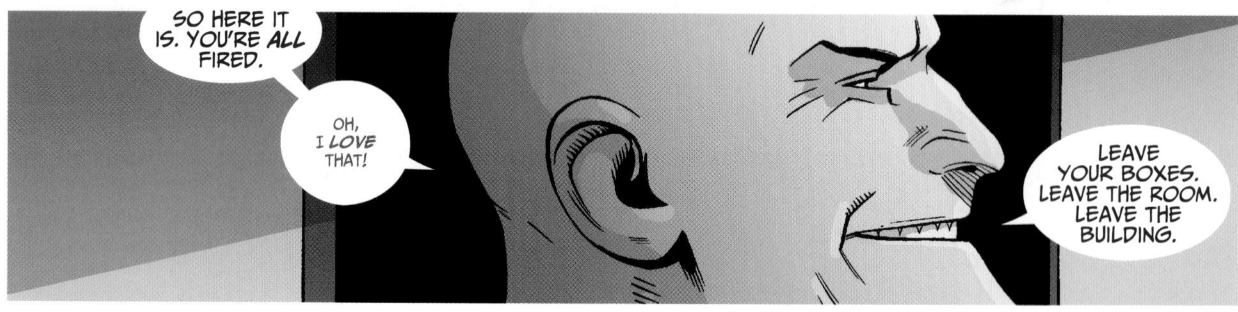

SO HERE IT IS. YOU'RE ALL FIRED.
OH, I LOVE THAT!
LEAVE YOUR BOXES. LEAVE THE ROOM. LEAVE THE BUILDING.

SUPES HAS BEEN FIGHTING THAT THING ALL MORNIN'!

IT KEEPS TAKING EVERYTHING HE THROWS AT IT! GETS UP AND COMES BACK FOR MORE!

12:15 PM - FINISH UP THE MORNING'S LAB-WORK IN R&D
YOU KNOW, MICHELLE? LUNCH DOESN'T TASTE THE SAME UNLESS YOU'VE FINISHED THE MORNING BY PUNCHING THROUGH A RETAINING WALL OF TECHNOLOGY OR PHYSICS.
THIS, THIS IS GROUNDBREAKING.

I MEAN THAT LITERALLY. THIS LASER COULD CUT THE MOON IN HALF.
NOT THAT I INTEND TO, BUT IT'S NICE TO KNOW I COULD IF I WANTED.
SIR, ARE YOU EVER CONCERNED THAT MOST OF THE THINGS YOU INVENT ARE DESTRUCTIVE, RATHER THAN FOR THE BETTERMENT OF MANKIND AS A SPECIES?

MICHELLE, ARE YOU EVER CONCERNED THAT YOU COME ACROSS AS WHINEY?
12:16 PM - HIRE NEW P.A.

UGHNNNN!

1:00 PM - LUNCH SUMMIT WITH SELECT WORLD LEADERS
BAM

OUTRAGEOUS! THIS IS NOT THE PRICE WE NEGOTIATED WITH LEXCORP FOR THE WEAPONS EXPORT PACKAGE! IT'S THREE TIMES THE FIRST INSTALLMENT--
WHAT CAN I SAY? THE ECONOMY IS IN FLUX.
I DON'T HAVE TO TELL YOU ABOUT BANANA FUTURES.
SO... THE SECOND INSTALLMENT IS GOING TO COST MORE.

AND THE THIRD WILL PROBABLY COST EVEN MORE AGAIN.
BUT THE WEAPONS YOU TOOK DELIVERY OF IN THE FIRST INSTALLMENT ARE FITTED WITH FAILSAFE SWITCHES.
SO I CAN DETONATE THEM AT ANY TIME. ARE WE SEEING THE PICTURE?

WE WILL PAY WHATEVER YOU ASK.
GREAT.
BY THE WAY, THE BANOFFEE HERE IS SUBLIME.

7:30 PM - SOAK UP A LITTLE CULTURE
SO, LEX, DID YOU SEE MY LAST MOVIE?
I'VE SEEN EVERYTHING YOU'VE EVER BEEN IN, INCLUDING ELEVATORS, LIMOUSINES AND BATHTUBS. I TEND TO CAREFULLY PRE-SURVEIL MY DATES.
HUH?

NEVER MIND.
DON'T YOU LIKE OPERA? YOU'RE JUST WRITING IN THAT BOOK. WHAT'S SO IMPORTANT YOU HAVE TO WRITE IT DOWN?

THINGS YOUR BRAIN WOULD NOT COMPREHEND IF IT SPENT TEN MILLION YEARS EVOLVING.
I'M GOING NOW BECAUSE YOU'RE BORING AND I'VE HAD A GREAT IDEA.
SEE YOURSELF HOME.

10:30 PM - DOWNTIME IN THE OFFICE AFTER HOURS

THAT'S WHEN A LOT OF THE VERY **BEST** THINKING GETS DONE. IN THE STILLNESS OF THE NIGHT WHEN THERE'S NOTHING TO DISTURB--

KKRAAATISSHH

I KNOW IT WAS YOU, LUTHOR.
I KNOW YOU BUILT THAT THING.

PROVE IT.

WE BOTH KNOW I CAN'T.
YOU'LL HAVE COVERED YOUR TRACKS TOO WELL.

UNLESS YOU'VE LEFT BLUEPRINTS OR DESIGNS SOMEWHERE...
OF COURSE. EVERYTHING'S LEAD-LINED.

EVEN YOUR NOTEBOOK HAS A LEAD COVER.

IT'S VERY PRIVATE!

YEEOOOW!
FSSSSHH

THAT WAS WANTON VANDALISM! UTTERLY WANTON!

PROVE IT.

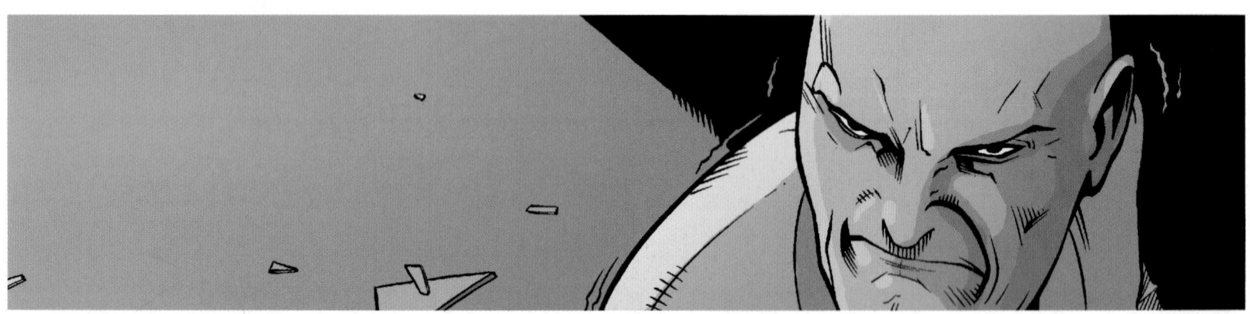

AND YOU'LL PAY FOR THE WINDOW!

INSUFFERABLE.
IRRITATING.
INFURIATING.

AND YOU WERE A WORTHLESS IDEA!

MR. LUTHOR! SIR! ARE YOU OKAY?

SHHH! DON'T INTERRUPT! I'VE HAD AN IDEA...

HOW TO KILL
SUPERMAN
IDEA #78014

END

LEX LUTHOR

ALTER EGOS: None
BASE OF OPERATIONS: Mobile

POWERS/ABILITIES: As Luthor would tell you himself, the only thing he needs is his mind, which is one of the most dangerous weapons on the planet.

HISTORY: After a secretive **FORMATIVE LIFE** in Smallville, Lex Luthor disappeared for years before emerging in the city of Metropolis as this era's greatest scientific mind. Lex Luthor was the hero of the city of tomorrow, but that all changed when people believed a man could fly.

Infuriated that Superman was hailed as an inspiration to humanity, Luthor became obsessed with destroying him. Many times, Luthor has claimed that he can solve the world's ills but refuses to do so until Superman is out of his way. At first, Luthor was able to attack Superman without getting his hands dirty, but recently his villainy has been publicly exposed. He was arrested and imprisoned like a common criminal.

In the wake of General Zod's attack on Earth and later the formation of New Krypton, Luthor was forcibly recruited by **GENERAL LANE** because of his knowledge of how to kill Kryptonians. While being held in Project 7734, Luthor made contact with another of Lane's captives, the alien **BRAINIAC**. They have made an unknown agreement during this time.

Luthor has studied the "dead" body of **DOOMSDAY**, but so far has failed to realize what secret it holds. This is most likely because of his preoccupation with another experiment he's been working on — Project: Alien Farm.

Text by GEOFF JOHNS, art by FRANCIS MANAPUL, color by BRIAN BUCCELLATO

BRAINIAC

ALTER EGO: None

BASE OF OPERATIONS: The known and unknown universe

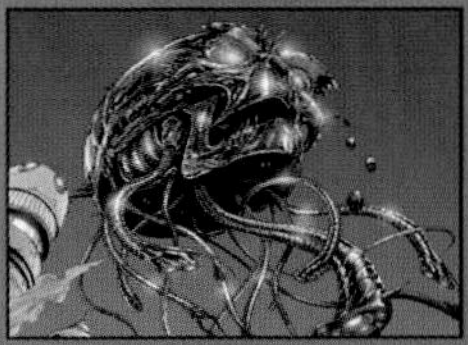

POWERS/ABILITIES: Brainiac has 12th level intelligence, an unmatched intellect beyond superhuman. In addition, his collective knowledge of technology, bioengineering and theoretical science has led to self-genetic-manipulation. Brainiac is as strong and invulnerable as a Kryptonian as long as he is in relative contact with his bio-shell i.e. **SPACECRAFT**. Though his physical fighting style appears lumbering and awkward, it is effective.

HISTORY: The cold, emotionless Coluan alien known as Brainiac is centuries old. Over those centuries, he set out to collect information, using it to evolve himself into the highest form of intelligent life. Brainiac's modus operandi is to "shrink" a city and destroy the planet it comes from, thereby ensuring no one can share the information he possesses. These **"BOTTLE CITIES"** are suspended within his craft and tethered directly into his brain, where he absorbs and sorts all data they contain. One such planet he attacked was Krypton.

Brainiac targeted its intelligence capital, Kandor City, and stole it. Days later, the planet Krypton was destroyed. Although natural causes were assumed to be the cause of Krypton's death, Superman still speculates that Brainiac was responsible.

Years later, Brainiac learned of the survival of Kal-El. Unwilling to share Krypton's knowledge, Brainiac launched a series of **PROBES** in search of the Kryptonian survivor. Although they encountered the Man of Steel, they were unable to report his location. Ultimately, it was Superman who went after Brainiac after learning he held Kandor. Superman freed the city, but at a terrible price. With the Man of Steel distracted, Brainiac attempted to destroy Superman's parents, Jonathan and Martha Kent. His attack failed, but in the process, **JONATHAN** suffered a fatal heart attack after saving his wife.

Brainiac was brought to General Lane's Project 7734 for further study. After Brainiac murdered Lane's initial group of scientists, General Lane brought in someone he deemed expendable if such an event were to happen again – Lex Luthor.

Brainiac is not truly comatose as everyone believes. The Coluan alien will stop at nothing to regain his Bottle Cities and destroy all of Krypton — or New Krypton. Whatever the case may be.

Text by GEOFF JOHNS, art by FRANCIS MANAPUL, color by BRIAN BUCCELLATO

"EVERY LIFE TRAVELS AT SUPERSPEED, I GUESS...

"ONE MINUTE YOUR CHILD'S A BABY.

"NOT A CARE IN THE WHOLE WIDE WORLD.

JSJS1

"THEN ONE DAY YOU BLINK AND...

"...WELL...

"...I DO SO WORRY ABOUT MY BOY, LET ME JUST SAY THAT."

SAVIOR

Rob Williams · Writer Chris Weston · Artist
Wes Abbott · Letterer Alex Antone · Editor
Bruce Timm & Nick Filardi · Cover

Superman created by
Jerry Siegel & Joe Shuster
By special arrangement
with the Jerry Siegel Family.

YOUR INCONSEQUENTIAL ADOPTED HOME AND YOUR POWER BASE, KRYPTONIAN, WILL *NOT* SURVIVE WHEN I, BRAINIAC...

...AUGMENT THE TECHNOLOGY OF THE HUBBLE SPACE TELESCOPE AND SHRINK YOUR YELLOW SUN TO THE SIZE OF A HUMAN HEART!!!

"HE DOES GET HIMSELF INTO SUCH SCRAPES..."

YES!

BEGIN THE SUN-SHRINKING PROCEDURE!!!

FEEL IT, KRYPTONIAN!!!

FEEL YOUR ADOPTIVE POWER WHITHER BEFORE THE CELESTIAL GLORY OF INTELLECT!

"BUT, ONE OF THE REASONS I ALWAYS HAVE SUCH *FAITH* IN HIM..."

NNNNN...

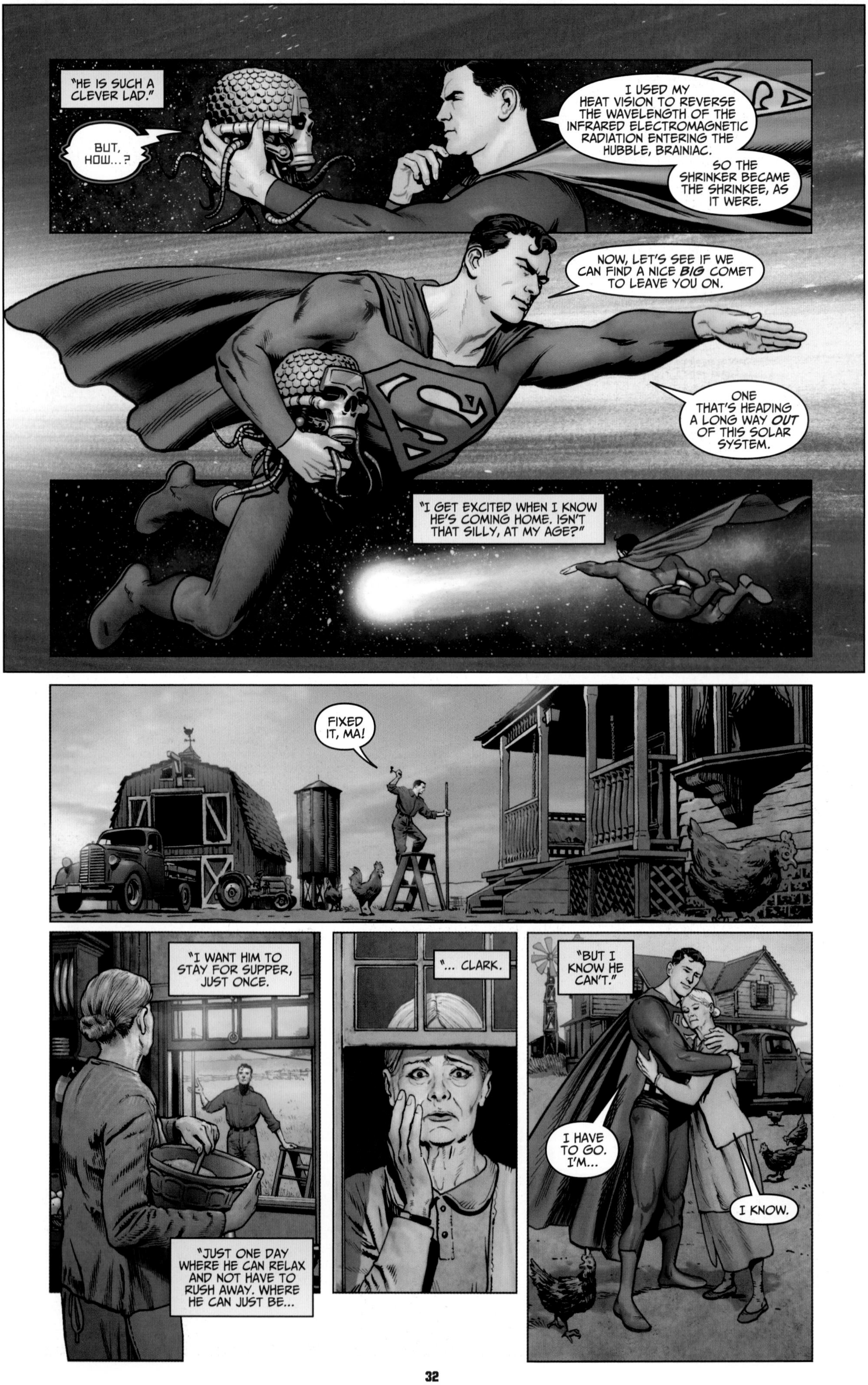

"HE IS SUCH A CLEVER LAD."

BUT, HOW...?

I USED MY HEAT VISION TO REVERSE THE WAVELENGTH OF THE INFRARED ELECTROMAGNETIC RADIATION ENTERING THE HUBBLE, BRAINIAC.

SO THE SHRINKER BECAME THE SHRINKEE, AS IT WERE.

NOW, LET'S SEE IF WE CAN FIND A NICE *BIG* COMET TO LEAVE YOU ON.

ONE THAT'S HEADING A LONG WAY *OUT* OF THIS SOLAR SYSTEM.

"I GET EXCITED WHEN I KNOW HE'S COMING HOME. ISN'T THAT SILLY, AT MY AGE?"

"THERE IS *ALWAYS* SOMEONE WHO NEEDS SAVING..."

THANK YOU FOR FIXING THE LINE.

YOU'RE WELCOME...

"I SUPPOSE I'M NOT THE FIRST OLD LADY TO SEE HER SON HEAD OFF TO THE BIG BAD CITY.

"SO MANY DANGERS..."
DAILY PLANET
GREAT CAESAR'S GHOST!!!

KENT!
PERRY WHITE
EDITOR
KENT!!!

KENT!
FOR TEN BUCKS I AM WILLING TO CAUSE A DISTRACTION SO YOU CAN RUN BEFORE HE SEES.
ACTUALLY, FORGET IT, HE'S ON ONE OF HIS RHINO CHARGES. NO WAY YOU'RE FAST ENOUGH.

THE JUDGE IN THE SALLY BERKOFF CASE JUST DID A LAST-SECOND ABOUT-FACE AND LET THE KIDNAPPING GOON WALK FREE! AND THEY STILL HAVEN'T FOUND THE KID!
I WANT A STORY CONTAINING EVERYTHING WE HAVE ON JUDGE CAMPBELL IN 15 MINUTES! GIMME REASONS HE COULD BE IN THE POCKET OF THE MOB!
YES, MR. WHITE!

AND SPELL ABHORRENT PROPERLY!!
UH... CHIEF?
IF YOU WANT, I COULD HEAD DOWN TO CITY HALL AND TAKE SOME SHOTS OF...

YES, PLEASE, OLSEN, THREE SUGARS...
WHERE THE HELL IS LANE WHEN I NEED HER? WASN'T SHE OFF DIGGING INTO THE KIDNAPPER'S PAST?

LOIS...
"I OFTEN WONDER WHAT AN AVERAGE DAY FOR HIM MUST BE..."

"HOW MANY PEOPLE MUST CRY OUT TO HIM."
STAY ABOVE THE... NNNNFF... WATER... SALLY...

I'M TRYING, MISS LANE!
STUPID... LOUSY... LEAD-LINED PIT!

YOU SHOULDN'T 'A COME SNOOPING, LADY!
STICK IT IN YOUR EAR!!

MISS LANE... ARE YOU OKAY?
"DESPITE EVERYTHING. ALL HIS GIFTS. HE'S STILL JUST ONE MAN.

"HE CAN'T BE EVERYWHERE..."

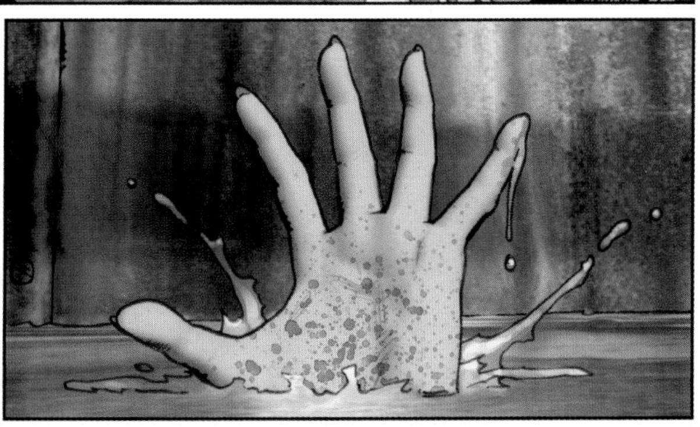

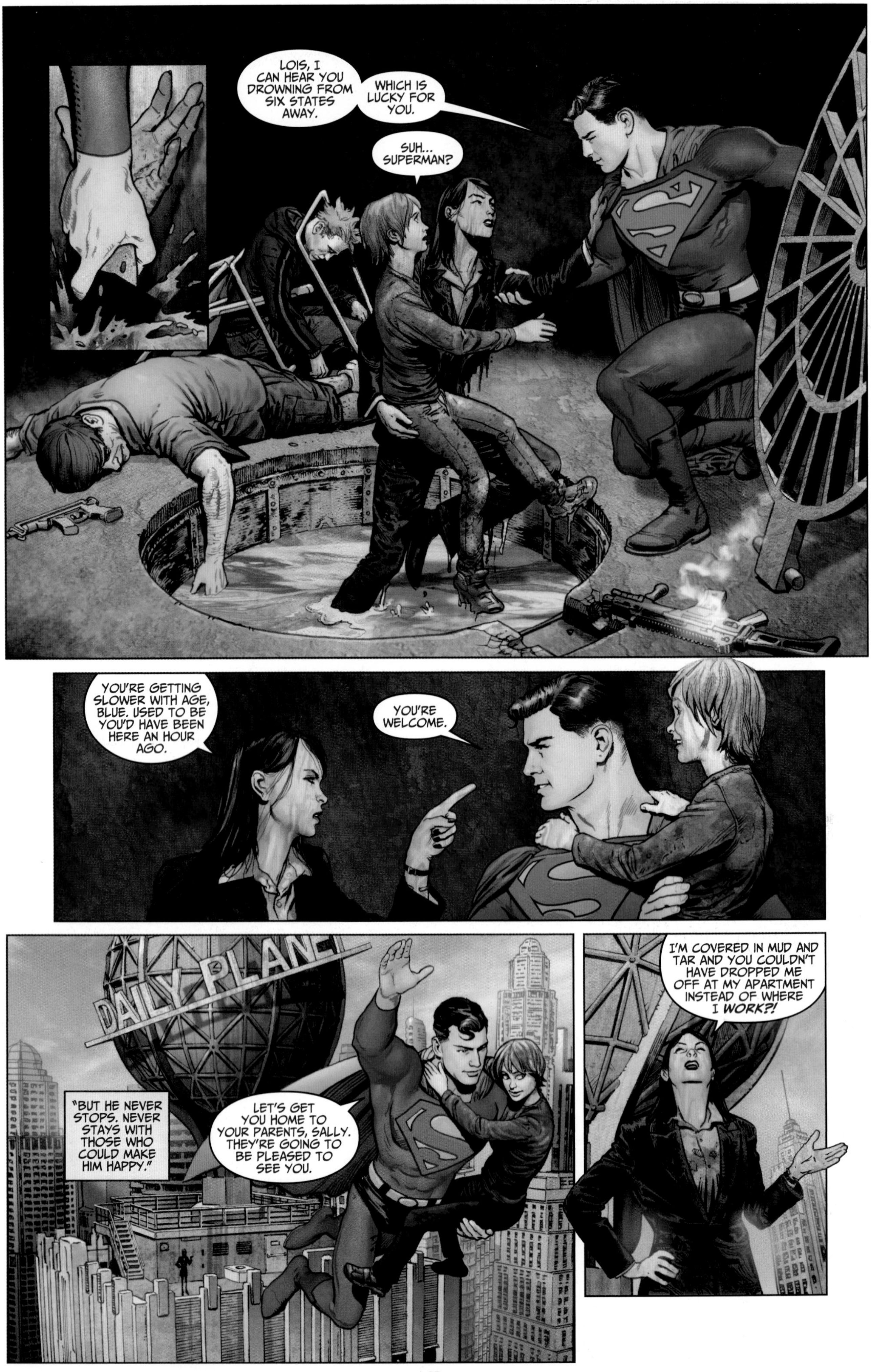

LOIS, I CAN HEAR YOU DROWNING FROM SIX STATES AWAY.
WHICH IS LUCKY FOR YOU.
SUH... SUPERMAN?

"JUST HOW MANY PEOPLE CAN HE SAVE?"
IT'S GORILLA GRODD, SUPERMAN! AND HIS *WINGED APE ARMY!!*

"FLYING FROM ONE PLACE TO THE NEXT."
YOU CANNOT COMPETE WITH THE POWER OF *ULTIMATE HATE,* JUSTICE LEAGUE.
SHALL WE?
LEAD THE WAY.

"NEVER STOPPING."
BIZARRO AM IN NO WAY ASHAMED TO BE ELECTED THE OLD PRESIDENT OF THE DIVIDED STATES!
TOMORROW WE NOT INVADE CANADA!

"MOVING SO FAST..."
AAIIIIEEEE!!!
IT'S A GIANT, BALD ROBOT!!!!

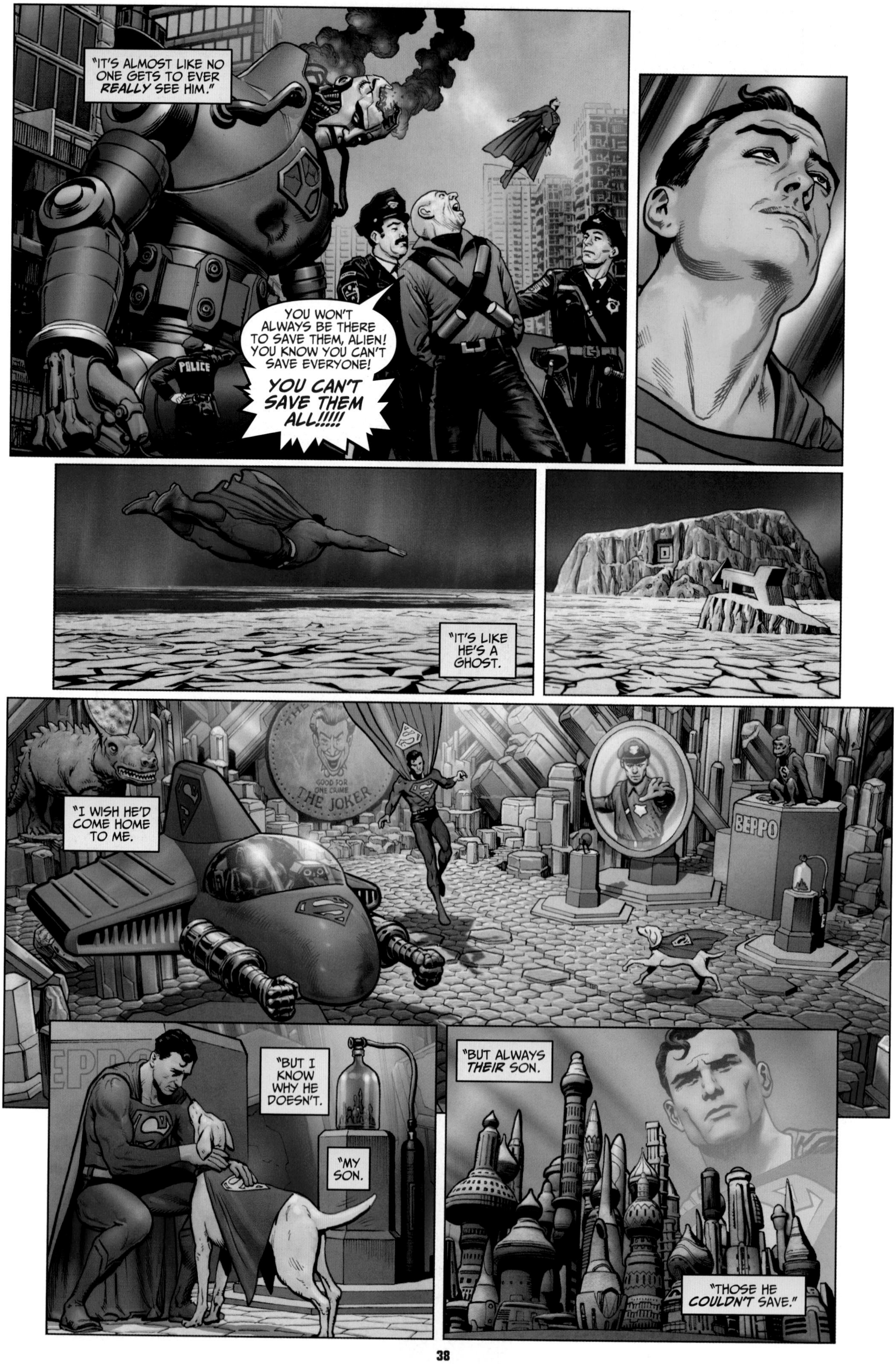

"IT'S ALMOST LIKE NO ONE GETS TO EVER *REALLY* SEE HIM."
POLICE
YOU WON'T ALWAYS BE THERE TO SAVE THEM, ALIEN! YOU KNOW YOU CAN'T SAVE EVERYONE!
YOU CAN'T SAVE THEM ALL!!!!!

"IT'S LIKE HE'S A GHOST.

"I WISH HE'D COME HOME TO ME.

THE JOKER

GOOD FOR ONE CRIME

BEPPO

"BUT I KNOW WHY HE DOESN'T.

"MY SON.

"BUT ALWAYS *THEIR* SON.

"THOSE HE *COULDN'T* SAVE."

UH...
HI.

I...UH...WAS WONDERING IF THERE WAS ANY SUPPER LEFT?
RRRRR...
WELL, WE BOTH WERE.

LET'S GO INSIDE.

THANKS, MA.
YOU'RE A LIFESAVER.
THE END

THE DAILY PLANET

BASE OF OPERATIONS: Corner of 5th Avenue and Concord Lane, Downtown Metropolis

The Daily Planet is one of America's oldest and most respected news sources. The tabloid newspaper The Daily Star and WGBS-TV (both owned by media mogul Morgan Edge) are the Planet's main competitors.

LOIS LANE INVESTIGATIVE REPORTER — The daughter of **GENERAL SAM LANE** and Ella Lane, Lois is arguably the finest reporter at The Daily Planet. It was Lois who dubbed Metropolis's mysterious new flying man "Superman," and it was her first interview with him that revealed him to the world.

Following her engagement to fellow reporter Clark Kent, he revealed to her what she had suspected all along: that he was secretly Superman. The two have been happily married ever since, and Lois is now the only reporter to whom Superman will give interviews.

Recently, Lois learned that her sister **LUCY** had been masquerading as the Kryptonian villain **SUPERWOMAN**. Lois has started an investigation into Lucy's whereabouts, but so far has turned up nothing. She does suspect, however, that her supposedly dead father might have been involved in Lucy's seeming descent into madness.

RON TROUPE POLITICAL ANALYST — Ron Troupe is the most skilled political reporter at The Daily Planet. He has been on a self-imposed educational sabbatical the last few years, only recently returning to the Planet after earning his sixth degree. With his return, he began a series of articles exposing the seedy underbelly of Metropolis's politics. These haven't made him any friends in local government, and most politicians agree that it would be tragic if something bad were to happen to "Troupe the Snoop."

LANA LANG BUSINESS EDITOR — As Clark Kent's childhood sweetheart, Lana Lang was the first person outside of his parents to learn of his abilities. When Clark left Smallville for Metropolis, Lana stayed in Smallville, eventually earning a business degree and marrying local politics' rising star Pete Ross. Following Pete's brief time as President of the United States — he completed disgraced Lex Luthor's term — Lana and Pete divorced, and Pete returned to Smallville with their infant son.

Lana moved to Metropolis where she became the new CEO of LexCorp, quickly finding herself the target of several attacks meant for Luthor, including an assault by the alien villain Insect Queen.

Later, after dispatching some of LexCorp's men to aid Superman in his epic battle against Atlas, Lana was fired from her position. Perry White, seeing a valuable asset in Lana, quickly made her the editor of the Planet's Business section.

Lana recently took Clark's cousin, Kara, under her wing, but she might not be able to help Kara for very long, as she's started exhibiting some potentially ominous symptoms . . .

Text by STERLING GATES, art by JAMAL IGLE & JON SIBAL, color by NEI RUFFINO

PERRY WHITE EDITOR-IN-CHIEF — Born in the area of Metropolis known as Suicide Slum, Perry White became a copy boy at The Daily Planet when he was only a child. He worked his way up steadily, eventually becoming the youngest editor-in-chief in the history of the paper when he was in his early 30s.

Perry lives and breathes news, always pushing his reporters to write the best story. Though he can be temperamental and overly gruff with his staff, Perry genuinely cares for them and does his best to foster their abilities. Even Olsen.

JIMMY OLSEN STAFF PHOTOJOURNALIST — All Jimmy Olsen's ever wanted to be is a reporter. He was hired at an early age to work for the Planet, but it wasn't until he started taking photos of Superman that he got anyone's attention.

His friendship with Superman has helped his photography career flourish over the last few years, and recently Jimmy managed to convince Perry to let him investigate a story. That led him to Codename: Assassin, who Jimmy found out works for an organization called 7734, which is hellbent on destroying Superman.

Jimmy has yet to write his story on 7734, and if Codename: Assassin has anything to say about it, Jimmy won't be breathing long enough to type the byline.

CAT GRANT ENTERTAINMENT AND GOSSIP COLUMNIST — Cat Grant moved to Metropolis with her son, Adam, six weeks to the day her divorce was finalized. Formerly an entertainment columnist for the Los Angeles Tattler, she soon joined the Daily Planet and was reporting on the Metropolis elite. When a malfunctioning **TOYMAN** robot killed her son, however, a grieving Cat moved back to the West Coast.

Cat recently came back to Metropolis, announcing her return to the Planet with a bombastic article titled "Why the World Doesn't Need Supergirl." Since then, her outlandish pieces on the Girl of Steel have constantly been on the front page, but with Supergirl spending more and more time on New Krypton, it's been getting harder for Cat to write her pieces.

STEVE LOMBARD SPORTS REPORTER — Steve Lombard quit college when he was 20 years old to accept his dream job: starting quarterback for the Metropolis Sharks. But when a car accident shattered Steve's knees, he returned to college and earned a journalism degree, eventually landing a job as a sports reporter for The Daily Planet.

Steve can be extremely abrasive, but underneath all those bad jokes and insulting pranks is a man who really cares... about himself.

KRYPTO

ALTER EGO: Pal
BASE OF OPERATIONS: Smallville, Kansas

POWERS/ABILITIES: As it does to Kryptonians, the yellow sun empowers Krypto with flight, super-strength and an array of super-sensory powers. However, Superman would say Krypto's greatest ability is loyalty.

HISTORY: Before Superman was rocketed off the doomed Krypton, his father **JOR-EL** sent the House of El family dog, Krypto, on a test flight. Tragically, the rocket was lost in space and Krypto drifted for years until the ship's guidance system picked up a Kryptonian signal from Kal-El's rocket, which was now on Earth in Smallville. The rocket containing Krypto arrived, much to a **YOUNG CLARK KENT'S** surprise.

Krypto often assisted Clark during his teenage years as Superboy in Smallville and beyond – though, like Clark, he was never publicly known.

Kryptonian canines age very slowly, and Krypto is still active in the life of Superman and his family. Currently, Krypto lives with **MARTHA KENT** at her farmhouse and is overjoyed at the return of the current Superboy, Conner Kent.

Krypto has no known enemies...yet.

Text by GEOFF JOHNS, art by FRANCIS MANAPUL
color by BRIAN BUCCELLATO

DELANEY & LEIGH/01

ON A NORMAL DAY, YOU DON'T SEE FLYING SAUCERS IN THE NIGHT SKY (CERTAINLY NOT IN HAYEKVILLE, WISCONSIN).
YOU DON'T SEE THEM DROP, OUT OF CONTROL.
YOU DON'T SEE THEM CRASH VIOLENTLY TO EARTH.
BUT THERE'S NOTHING NORMAL ABOUT TODAY.
The Star-Conqueror
Todd Seavey - writer Chris Jones - pencils
Al Nickerson - inks Kurt Hathaway - letters
John Kalisz - colors Heroic Age - separations
Steve Wacker - assistant editor
Dan Raspler - editor

JUSTICE LEAGUE ADVENTURES 5. May, 2002. Published monthly by DC Comics, 1700 Broadway, New York, NY 10019. POSTMASTER: Send address changes to JUSTICE LEAGUE ADVENTURES, DC Comics Subscriptions, P.O. Box 0528, Baldwin, NY 11510. Annual subscription rate $23.88. Canadian subscribers must add $12.00 for postage and GST. GST # is R125921072. All foreign countries must add $12.00 for postage. U.S. funds only.

Printed in Canada.
DC Comics. A division of Warner Bros.–An AOL Time Warner Company

I'VE HEARD ABOUT THINGS LIKE THIS AN' HOW THE GOVERNMENT SENDS MEN TO HIDE THE EVIDENCE.
EXCUSE ME. SIR?
YOU SHOULD MOVE BACK TO A SAFE DISTANCE.
AIIEEE! ONE OF THE MEN IN BLACK! DON'T KILL ME! I'LL KEEP QUIET!
NO, WE'RE THE JUSTICE LEAGUE.
OH, SUPERMAN! OF COURSE!
WE TRACKED THIS VESSEL.
LOOKS LIKE THESE PARASITES ON THEIR FACES KILLED MOST OF THE CREW BEFORE THE CRASH. BUT ONE GREY ALIEN IS STILL ALIVE.

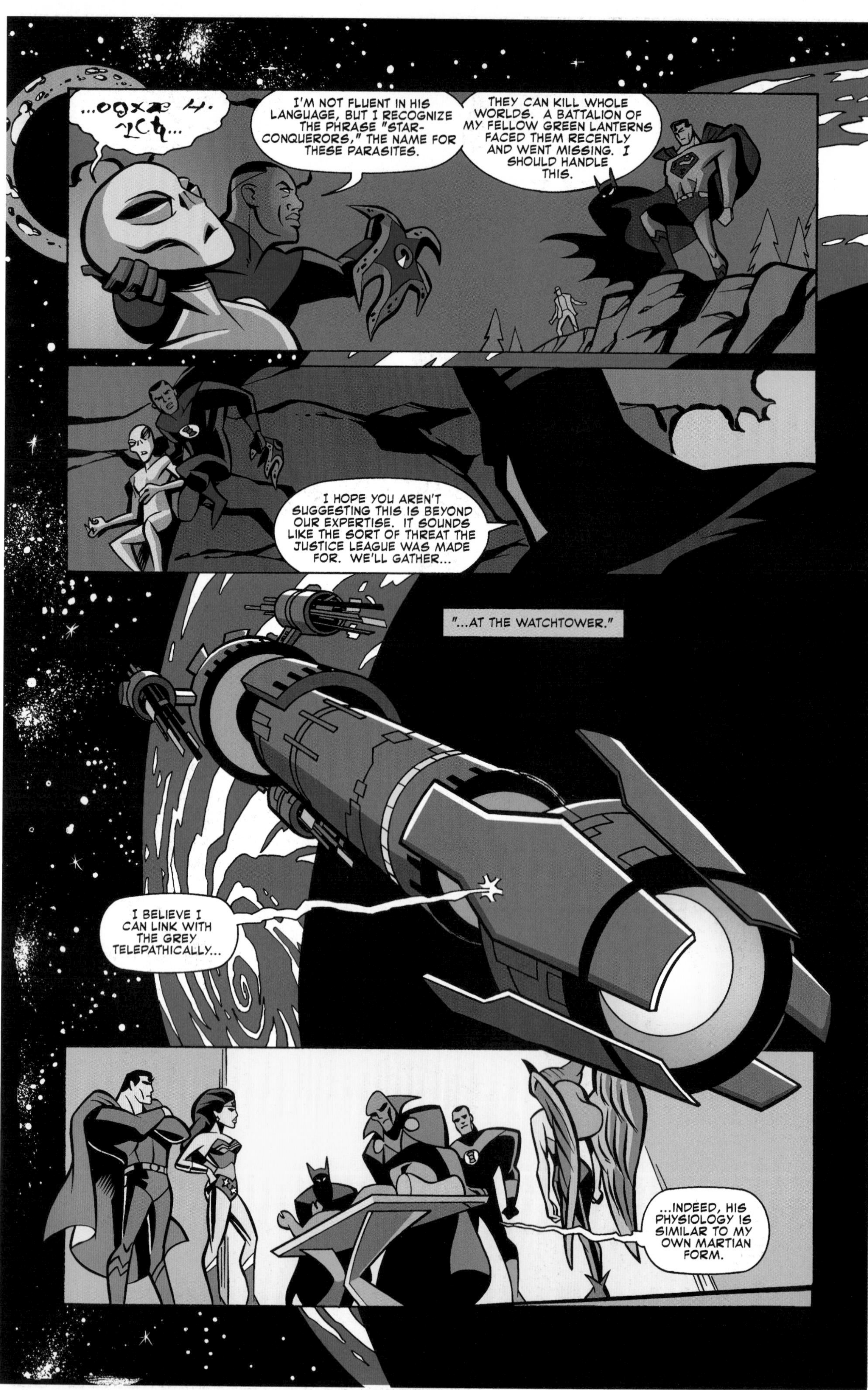
...ogxæ 4. ^ʟc̈ʰq...
I'M NOT FLUENT IN HIS LANGUAGE, BUT I RECOGNIZE THE PHRASE "STAR-CONQUERORS," THE NAME FOR THESE PARASITES.
THEY CAN KILL WHOLE WORLDS. A BATTALION OF MY FELLOW GREEN LANTERNS FACED THEM RECENTLY AND WENT MISSING. I SHOULD HANDLE THIS.
I HOPE YOU AREN'T SUGGESTING THIS IS BEYOND OUR EXPERTISE. IT SOUNDS LIKE THE SORT OF THREAT THE JUSTICE LEAGUE WAS MADE FOR. WE'LL GATHER...
"...AT THE WATCHTOWER."
I BELIEVE I CAN LINK WITH THE GREY TELEPATHICALLY...
...INDEED, HIS PHYSIOLOGY IS SIMILAR TO MY OWN MARTIAN FORM.

HE WAS FLEEING. HIS HOMEWORLD, THE GREY ORB, WAS OVERRUN BY THE PARASITES, WHICH DRIFTED DOWN FROM SPACE...
THEY DRAIN PSYCHIC ENERGY AND LIFEFORCE FROM THEIR UNWILLING HOSTS.
ONE STAR-CONQUEROR ABSORBS ALL THE ENERGY, GROWING IMMENSE, ALMOST INDESTRUCTIBLE, UNTIL IT BURSTS, SCATTERING MILLIONS OF OFFSPRING--NEW PARASITES--INTO HYPERSPACE, WHERE THEY DESCEND UPON A NEW TARGET-WORLD.
HUNGRY... SO...HUNGRY... THE GREY ORB...IS NOT ENOUGH...

I... WANT...YOUR... WORLD...
EARTH! SHE'LL TARGET HER OFFSPRING AT EARTH! THE GREYS CAME TO WARN US! I CAN HEAR HER... THROUGH HIS MIND...

A WHOLE WORLD'S PSYCHIC ENERGY AT HER DISPOSAL! UNHHH! ALL...TURNED TO... HUNGER...AND DEATH... RRRHHHH!
I'LL LOOK OVER J'ONN AND THE GREY AND MONITOR EARTH FOR ANY SIGN OF THE PARASITES. THE REST OF YOU BOARD THE JAVELIN...
"...AND HEAD TO THE GREY ORB TO STOP THIS THING."
OFF TO FIGHT THE GIANT-EVIL-PSYCHIC-ONE-EYED-EXTRATERRESTRIAL-STARFISH!
INTENSE!

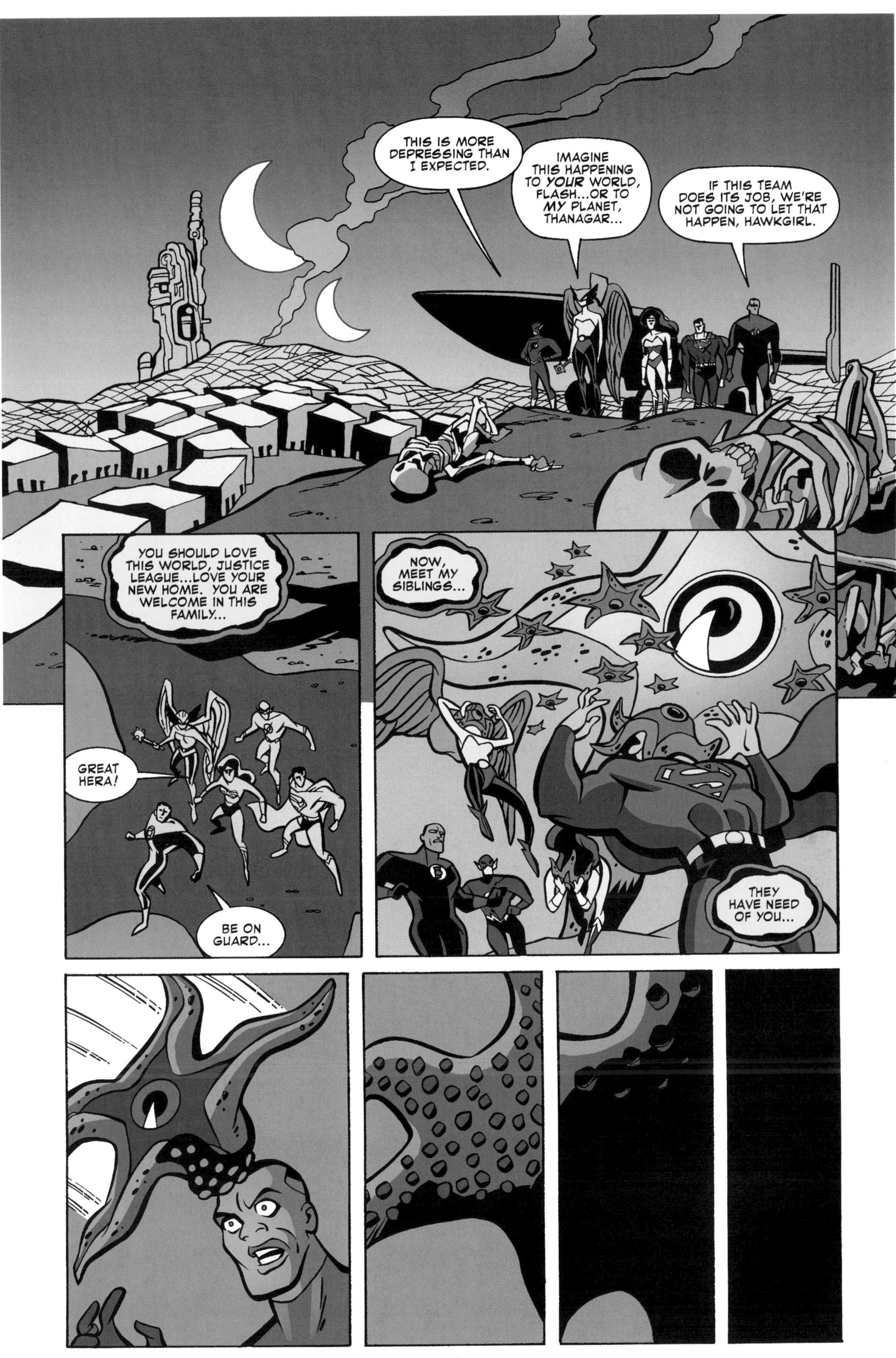
THIS IS MORE DEPRESSING THAN I EXPECTED.
IMAGINE THIS HAPPENING TO YOUR WORLD, FLASH...OR TO MY PLANET, THANAGAR...
IF THIS TEAM DOES ITS JOB, WE'RE NOT GOING TO LET THAT HAPPEN, HAWKGIRL.
YOU SHOULD LOVE THIS WORLD, JUSTICE LEAGUE...LOVE YOUR NEW HOME. YOU ARE WELCOME IN THIS FAMILY...
GREAT HERA!
BE ON GUARD...
NOW, MEET MY SIBLINGS...
THEY HAVE NEED OF YOU...

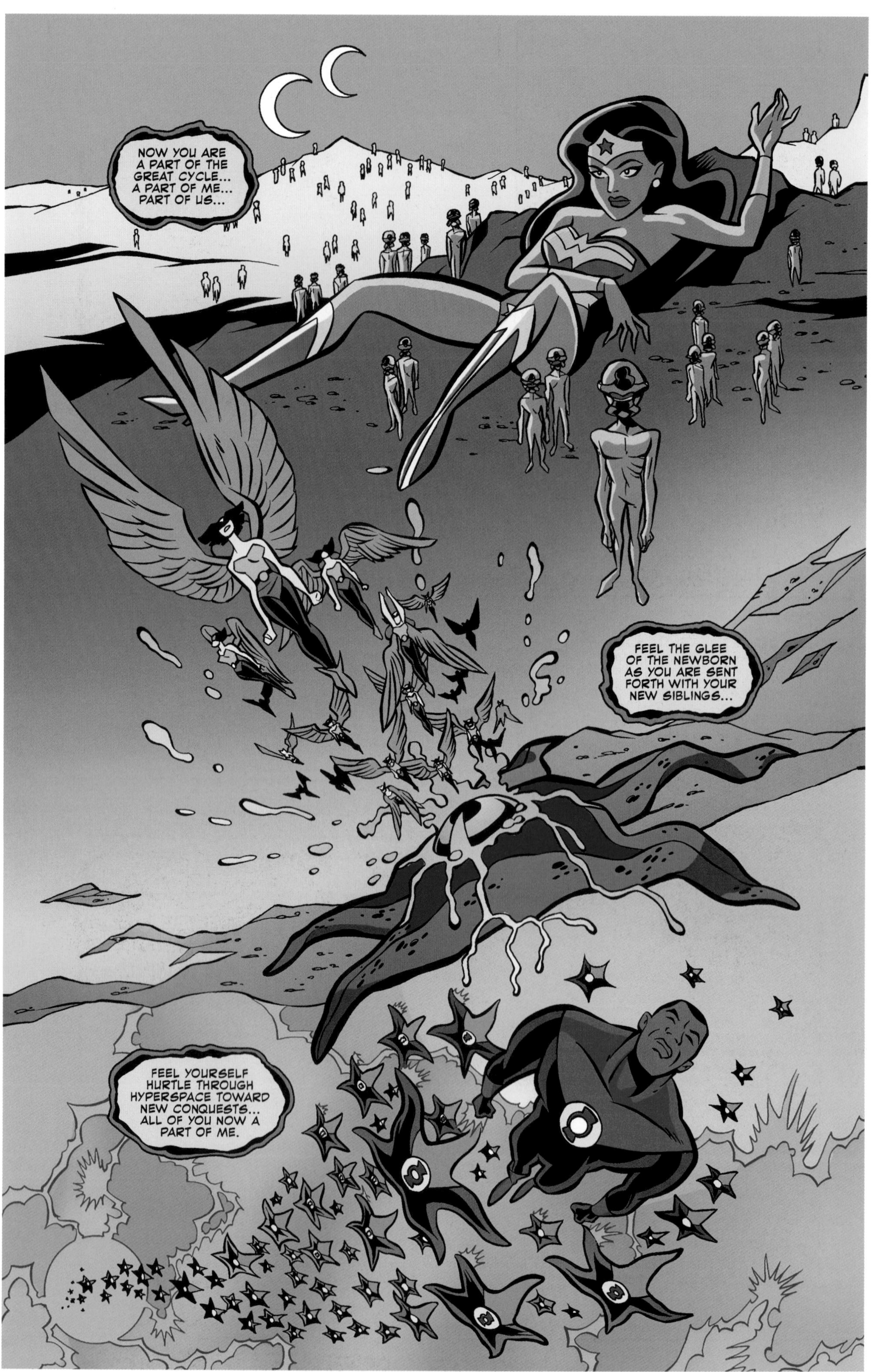
NOW YOU ARE A PART OF THE GREAT CYCLE... A PART OF ME... PART OF US...
FEEL THE GLEE OF THE NEWBORN AS YOU ARE SENT FORTH WITH YOUR NEW SIBLINGS...
FEEL YOURSELF HURTLE THROUGH HYPERSPACE TOWARD NEW CONQUESTS... ALL OF YOU NOW A PART OF ME.

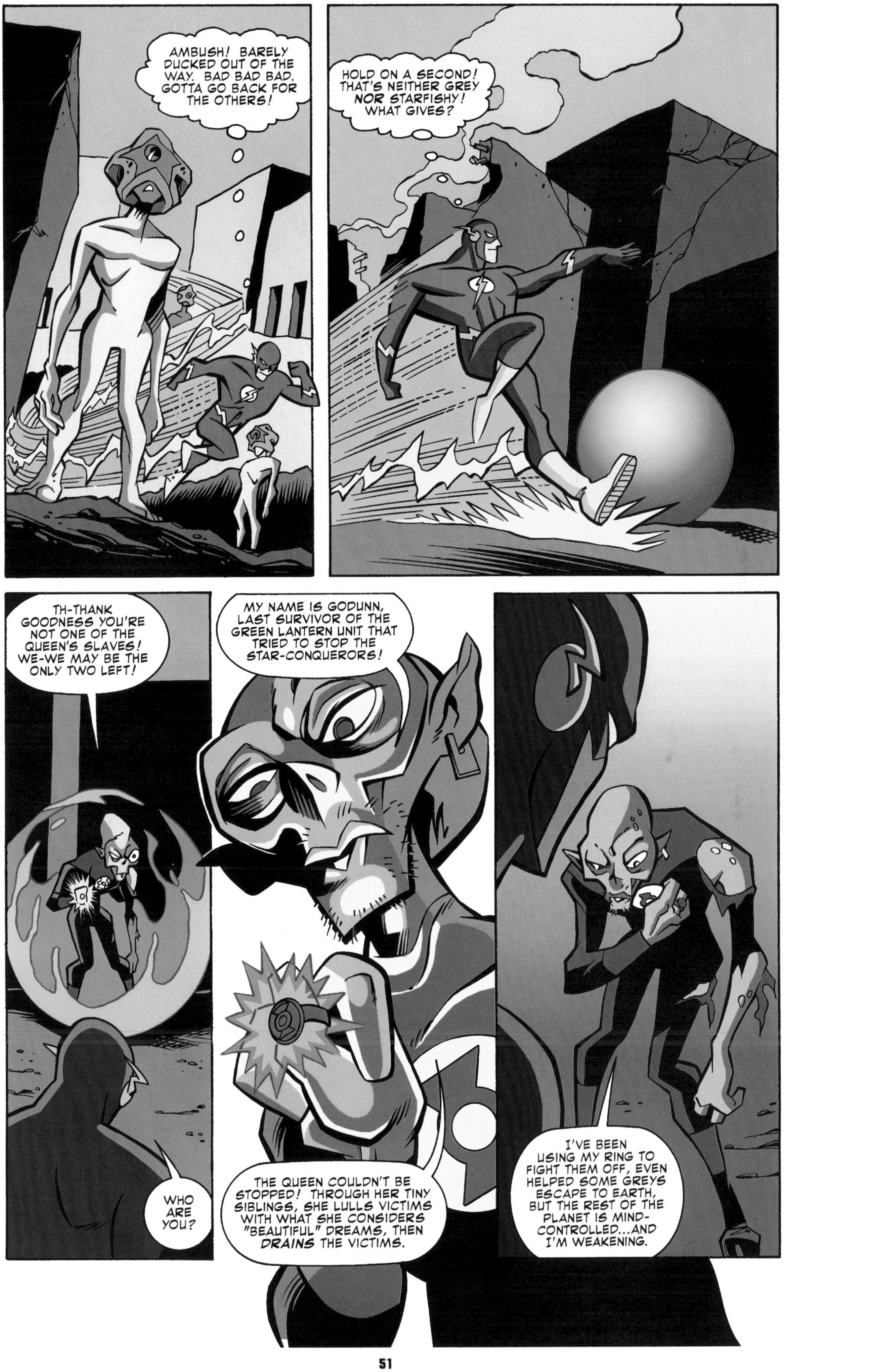

TH-THANK GOODNESS YOU'RE NOT ONE OF THE QUEEN'S SLAVES! WE-WE MAY BE THE ONLY TWO LEFT!

WHO ARE YOU?

MY NAME IS GODUNN, LAST SURVIVOR OF THE GREEN LANTERN UNIT THAT TRIED TO STOP THE STAR-CONQUERORS!

THE QUEEN COULDN'T BE STOPPED! THROUGH HER TINY SIBLINGS, SHE LULLS VICTIMS WITH WHAT SHE CONSIDERS "BEAUTIFUL" DREAMS, THEN *DRAINS* THE VICTIMS.

I'VE BEEN USING MY RING TO FIGHT THEM OFF, EVEN HELPED SOME GREYS ESCAPE TO EARTH, BUT THE REST OF THE PLANET IS MIND-CONTROLLED...AND I'M WEAKENING.

MY RING IS FUELED BY WILLPOWER... AND I CAN FEEL THE QUEEN DRAINING MY PSYCHIC ENERGY...
...WEAKENING ME MORE EVERY SECOND.
I HAVEN'T HAD ENOUGH POWER TO LAUNCH A FULL-SCALE ATTACK ON THE QUEEN, NOR ENOUGH TO FLEE THIS PLANET.
I HAVE POWERFUL FRIENDS WHO MAY BE ABLE TO STOP "STARRO" OVER THERE...BUT WE CAN'T STAY HIDDEN HERE.
AMAZING! YOU'RE AS FAST AS A GREEN LANTERN IN FLIGHT!
YEAH, NOW LET'S SEE IF I CAN OUTRUN A SCHOOL OF STARFISH!

PICTURE YOURSELF...FLOATING DOWN TO ATTACK A NEW WORLD...FLOATING LIKE A DUST MOTE...LIKE A LEAF...LIKE A CLOUD...
...LIKE A BIRD...LIKE A PLANE... LIKE...
...SUPERMAN! I'M SUPERMAN!
...SUPERMAN... I'M... SUPERMAN...

MAY ONLY HAVE A MOMENT--SUPERMAN LOOKS LIKE THE MOST LIKELY TO BENEFIT FROM AN ASSIST.
FREE...GOT TO FREE THE OTHERS BEFORE THE PARASITES RETURN.
FLASH! SUPERMAN! WELL DONE!
I'LL FREE HAWKGIRL...
...WHILE FLASH LIBERATES WONDER WOMAN.
EEEUGH!
NICE TO SEE YOU, TOO!

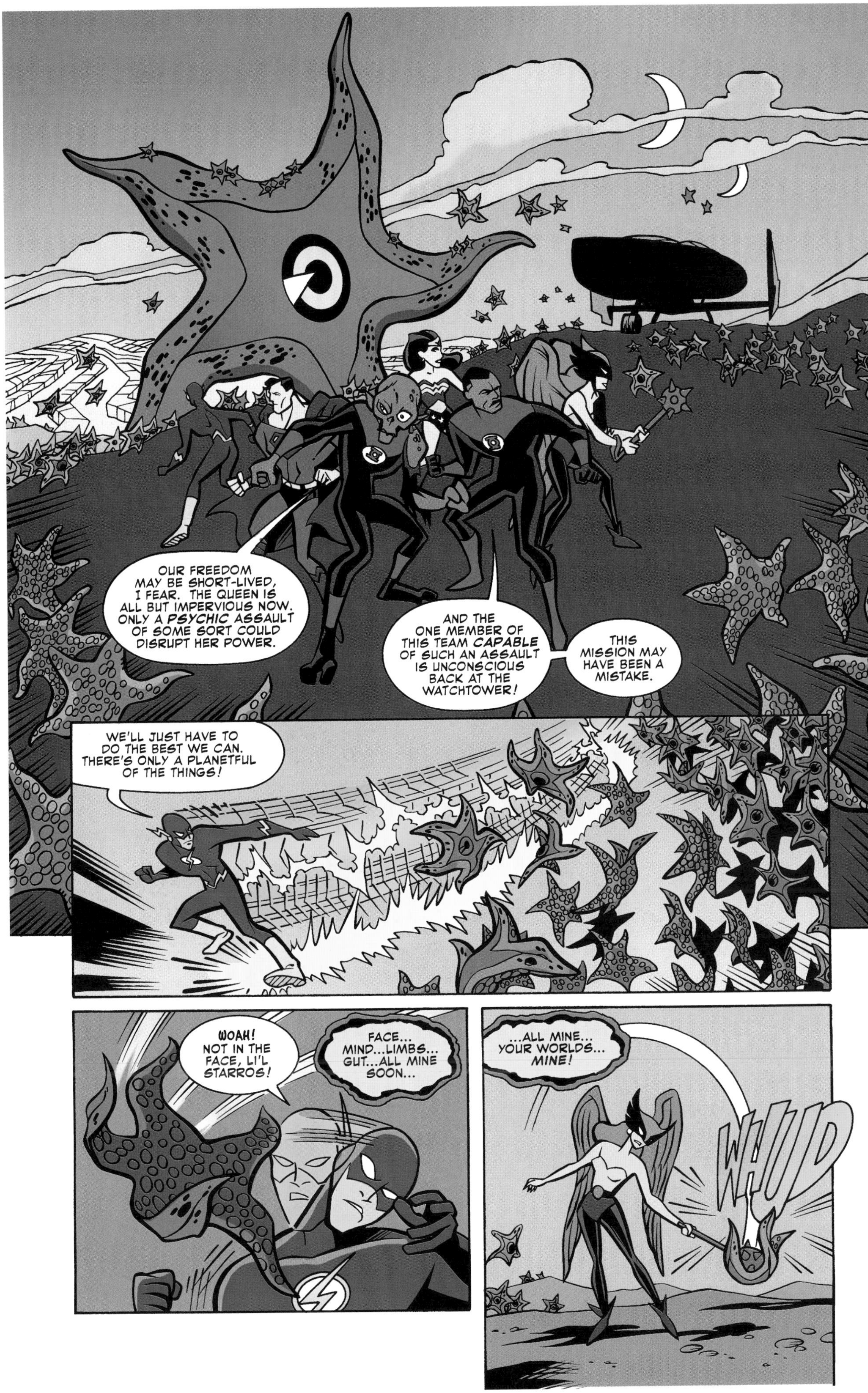

OUR FREEDOM MAY BE SHORT-LIVED, I FEAR. THE QUEEN IS ALL BUT IMPERVIOUS NOW. ONLY A *PSYCHIC* ASSAULT OF SOME SORT COULD DISRUPT HER POWER.

AND THE ONE MEMBER OF THIS TEAM *CAPABLE* OF SUCH AN ASSAULT IS UNCONSCIOUS BACK AT THE WATCHTOWER!

THIS MISSION MAY HAVE BEEN A MISTAKE.

WE'LL JUST HAVE TO DO THE BEST WE CAN. THERE'S ONLY A PLANETFUL OF THE THINGS!

WILL WE END UP ESCAPING WHILE THE GREY ORB DIES?
WILL I HAVE TO LEAVE THIS WORLD BEHIND AS I DID KRYPTON?
No!
WELCOME TO THE CHAIN OF LIFE, GODUNN... KILL FOR US...
ENOUGH! I HAVE NO MORE TIME TO WASTE FIGHTING PESTS.
TIME TO TAKE THE FIGHT TO THEIR QUEEN!

PARASITE! I HAVEN'T FORGOTTEN THE DREAMS YOU SENT US! ARE YOU FEEDING THE WHOLE POPULACE OF THIS PLANET THOSE LIES?
THIS LASSO FORCES YOU TO REVEAL THE TRUTH!
DO YOU SEE THEM? WAKING UP, ALL OVER THE WORLD, FROM THE DREAMING DEATH YOU IMPOSED...
WAKING TO THE NIGHTMARISH REALITY YOU'VE MADE OF THEIR PLANET?
SHE'S DONE IT! WEAKENED THE QUEEN! THIS IS MY CHANCE TO RECLAIM THE POWER THE QUEEN STOLE FROM MY RING!
GODUNN, WAIT! THE QUEEN IS STILL TOO STRONG, AND THE POWER INSIDE HER IS CORRUPTED. YOU'RE IN NO CONDITION TO CONTROL IT!

YOU DARE CALL ME PARASITE? OFF!
GOOD JOB, DIANA. THE GREYS ARE FREE. BUT I'M AFRAID THAT THING ALREADY HAS TOO MUCH POWER TO BE STOPPED.
I SHOULD HAVE COME HERE WITH THE ENTIRE GREEN LANTERN CORPS, NOT THE JUSTICE LEAGUE.
NOW THE QUEEN WILL FIND OUT WHAT IT FEELS LIKE TO BE DRAINED!
NO, GODUNN...ON THE CONTRARY...

...I AM ABOUT TO GIVE BIRTH...ALREADY A HYPERSPATIAL RIFT IS OPENING TO RECEIVE MY YOUNG...

SHE'S USING EVERY LAST BIT OF HER STRENGTH... TRYING TO KEEP THE POWER FROM ME... RING'S ABOUT TO EXPLODE FROM THE STRESS...SMALL PRICE TO PAY...
...IF IT STOPS HER...

SHE'S OPENING A PORTAL TO EARTH!
MORE THAN THAT, JOHN. SHE'S *BECOMING* A PORTAL TO EARTH!

IT'LL TAKE ALL THE POWER I'VE GOT--AND THE LEAGUE'S STRENGTH--BUT WE HAVE TO CLOSE THAT RIFT!
PAIN!!
DON'T LET THE EYE REOPEN!
THE OFFSPRING ARE BEGINNING TO BUD!
LOTS AND LOTS AND LOTS OF HOMICIDAL STARFISH!

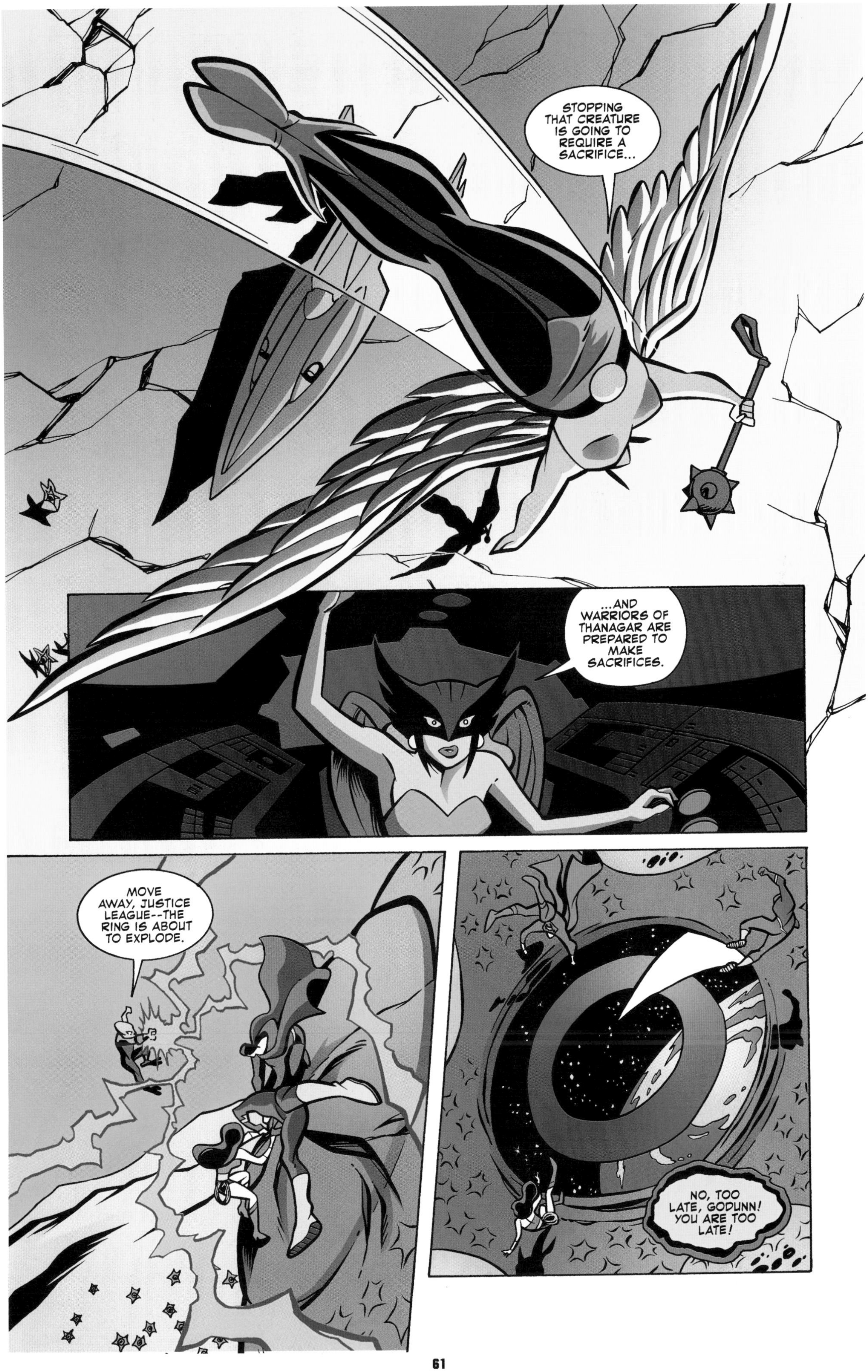

STOPPING THAT CREATURE IS GOING TO REQUIRE A SACRIFICE...

...AND WARRIORS OF THANAGAR ARE PREPARED TO MAKE SACRIFICES.

IT'S NOT TOO LATE FOR THIS, MONSTER!
TUMBLING... INTO THE RIFT!
AAARRRNNHHKKKK

THAT HURT YOU, MY QUEEN...
NOW FEEL THIS.
SNAARKOOM

DID YOU... DID YOU SEE IT? I PICKED IT UP ON THE MONITORS AS THE HYPERSPACE APERTURE WAS CLOSING. THE QUEEN WAS BLOWN APART.
AS WAS GODUNN. I COULD FEEL THE POWER SURGE AS HIS RING WAS DESTROYED.
BUT HE AVENGED HIS COMRADES, AND I HAVE TO ADMIT HE COULDN'T HAVE DONE IT WITHOUT THE LEAGUE.
WITH THE QUEEN DESTROYED, ALL THE OTHER PARASITES ON THE GREY ORB WILL DIE, TOO. GODUNN'S SACRIFICE WILL GIVE THE PLANET A SECOND SHOT AT LIFE.
THAT'S GOOD NEWS. LET'S HOPE PARASITES LIKE THOSE DON'T FIND THEIR WAY TO EARTH AGAIN SOMEDAY, DECADES OR CENTURIES FROM NOW.

SUPERMAN, IF THOSE THINGS EVER DO COME HERE, I HOPE THEY'LL FIND THE JUSTICE LEAGUE WAITING FOR THEM ...
"I'M PLEASED EARTH HAS HEROES WHO ARE AS BRAVE AS THE GREEN LANTERN CORPS.
"AND ON THE RARE OCCASIONS WHEN VISITORS COME TO US FROM OTHER WORLDS...
"...I HOPE THEY'LL TAKE STORIES OF THE JUSTICE LEAGUE BACK WITH THEM TO THE STARS."
THE
END

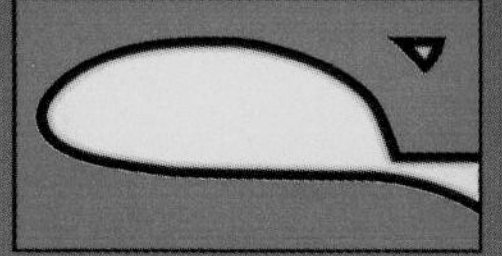

SUPERGIRL

ALTER EGOS: Kara Zor-El, Linda Lang

BASE OF OPERATIONS: New Krypton; Metropolis; formerly New York City

POWERS/ABILITIES: Supergirl possesses all of the powers of a Kryptonian under a yellow sun: flight, super strength, X-ray vision, heat vision, telescopic vision, invulnerability, and super speed. The full extent of some of these powers remains untested.

Text by STERLING GATES, art by JAMAL IGLE & JON SIBAL, color by NEI RUFFINO

HISTORY: Kara Zor-El was living happily with her parents **ZOR-EL** and **ALURA** in Argo City when **BRAINIAC** attacked Krypton and stole the city of Kandor. Within weeks, her uncle Jor-El declared the planet doomed, and her father Zor-El was working on a way to save Argo City in the event of Krypton's destruction. Krypton exploded weeks later.

Using Brainiac-based force field technology, Zor-El was able to keep Argo City intact, and the city floated adrift in space. Knowing the force field would one day fail, Zor began constructing a prototype rocket, with plans for mass-producing escape rockets for his people. His attempts were cut short when Brainiac discovered Argo and attacked. Alura and Zor-El quickly programmed the prototype rocket with the same coordinates Jor-El had used for his own son, Kal-El, and sent Kara off into space.

Unfortunately, Kara's rocket was struck by a massive piece of the exploding Argo City and was knocked off course. Arriving on Earth 30 years later, Kara found that her cousin was Superman, one of Earth's greatest heroes. Kara took on his heroic mantle to become Supergirl, and eventually took the secret identity of **LANA LANG'S** neice, **LINDA**.

During a fight on Brainiac's ship, Superman discovered Kara's parents were alive and well, living along with 100,000 other Kryptonians in the Bottle City of Kandor. Superman returned them to Earth. Kara's joyous reunion with her parents was short-lived, however, as the villain Reactron used his Gold Kryptonite-powered blasts to kill Zor-El.

Distraught, Alura created a new planet, which she dubbed New Krypton, and moved the displaced Kryptonians there. Kara elected to move to New Krypton, but her Earth ties keep pulling her back, even in light of the United Nations' decision to ban all Kryptonians.

Now, whenever Kara is on Earth, she spends time searching for Reactron. When she finds him, she will return him to New Krypton to face Kryptonian justice.

Supergirl has undergone extensive hand-to-hand training with Batman and the Amazonian warriors. Reunited with her people, Supergirl has also begun studying the Kryptonian martial art Klurkor, testing as high as first-degree badge.

75
75 YEARS OF BATMAN

SUPERMAN®
B.T.
NF